GOSPEL MASS

by ROBERT RAY

CONTENTS

Complete orchestration available
HL08743496 $125.00

I. KYRIE
LORD HAVE MERCY

ROBERT RAY

447-07014

11
Rock (♩=120)
vamp as necessary
One.
One.
Ab mi/Eb
Eb mi7
Ab mi7
Play
8vb
(8va optional)
Enter 2nd time
(Toms fill)
Hi-Hat

19
p
Oh 1. Lord have mer - cy.
2. Christ
Abmi7
(8va optional)
1. Ky - ri - e e - le - i-son.
2. Chri - ste
Oh 1. Lord have mer - cy.
2. Christ
2

25
Oh Lord have mercy on me. Send us a Savior, set my soul free. Give us Your word and teach us to pray.
Oh Christ have mercy on me. Send us Your comfort, grant us Your peace. You are the way, the truth and the light.
Lord,
Christ,
A♭mi7

33
I want to praise_ and serve___ You al - ways.
I love You more_ each day___ and each night.
Lord God of A - bra-ham, I - saac
Je - sus the Rock of sal - va - tion,
Abmi7
N.C.
for rehearsal only
and Ja - cob look down, have mer - cy up - on___ us.
the Light of the world, have mer - cy up - on___ us.
Dbmi7
Ebmi7
Db/Eb
p
mf
ff
fill
Cym.
(soft mallets)

1
to measure 19
2
1
2 A♭mi7
D♭/E♭
43
p - mf - f (repeat as desired)
Oh Lord_have mer - cy.
p - mf - f (repeat as desired)
Oh Lord_have mer - cy.
p - mf - f (repeat as desired)
Oh Lord_have mer - cy
p - mf - f (repeat as desired)
Oh Lord_have mer - cy.
A♭mi7
D♭/E♭
43
A♭mi7
p - mf - f (repeat as desired)

Ky - ri - e e - le - i - son.
Oh Christ have mer - cy.
A♭mi7
2
Chri - ste e - le - i - son.
Oh Lord have mer - cy.
rit.
(ride cym.)
(ad lib fill)

II. GLORIA
GLORY TO GOD IN THE HIGHEST

ROBERT RAY

we — a - dore Thee, — we — glo - ri - fy — Thee.
Bbmi7/Ab
Ab
Gmi7(b5)
C7
Tom fill
mf
13
We give thanks to Thee — for Thy great glo - ry.
We give thanks to Thee — for Thy great glo - ry.
We give thanks to Thee — for Thy great glo - ry.
We give thanks to Thee — for Thy great glo - ry.
C7
Db/Ab Eb/Ab
C#mi7
Bmi7
E
fill (Toms)
(Hi-Hat)

mp
We praise Thee, we bless Thee,
E E7 Amaj7 Bmi7/A D6/E Amaj7 Bmi7/A
mp
(sus. cym.)
(soft mallets)
mp H.H.
mp
we a - dore Thee, we glo - ri - fy Thee.
f
Bmi7/A A G♯mi7(♭5) C♯7
fill

25
Lord God, King, of heav'n Fa-ther, Al - might - y One..
C♯7 F♯mi/A E/A Dmaj7 C♯mi7 F♯mi
fill
Glo-ry be to Je - sus Christ, Lamb of God, the Fa - ther's on - ly Son.
Jesus Christ, Lamb of God, the Fa - ther's on-ly Son.
F♯mi Dmaj7 C♯mi7

high - est,
Glo-ry to God_ in the high - est, peace to all men_ of good will._
Glo-ry to God_ in the high - est, peace to all men_ of good will._
Glo-ry to God_ in the high - est, peace to all men_ of good will._
Glo-ry to God_ in the high - est, peace to all men_ of good will._
F♯
Dmaj7
(E♭)
(E♭13) (Dmaj13)
Bmi7/E
37 Slower (♩=84)
(Optional ad lib solo over choir)
1.,2. Thou who takes_ a - way all the
1.,2. Thou who takes_ a - way all the
1.,2. Thou who takes_ a - way all the
1.,2. Thou_ all,
Bmi7/E
E7
G/A
G/A
(ad lib cym. fills)
(soft mallets)

1.
rit.
sins of the world,
1. have mer - cy on us.
2. re - ceive our
G/A
F♯mi/A E
Dmaj7
C♯mi7
Bmi7
D/E
2.
prayers.
47
Thou who
(ad lib cym. fill if desired)

(𝅗𝅥=𝅗𝅥.)
sits at the right hand of God the Fa - ther Al - might - y in heav'n
sits at the right hand of God the Fa - ther Al - might - y in heav'n
sits at the right hand of God the Fa - ther Al - might - y in heav'n
sits at the right hand of God the Fa - ther Al - might - y in heav'n
G/A
have mer - cy on us.
have mer - cy on us.
have mer - cy on us.
have mer - cy on us.
F♯ mi/A E Dmaj7
C♯ mi7
Bmi7
D/E
S.D.
R.S.

(in 2)
57
Building Slowly (𝅗𝅥=66) (in 2)
p Gradual accelerando and crescendo to 66
For
On - ly Thou_art ho - ly,
on - ly Thou_art
1. the
2. most
(A)
Emi7/A
A
Emi7/A
Asus
Lord.
high.
(𝅗𝅥 =72)
On - ly Thou__art ho - ly,
(2nd time only)
fill

1.
2.
on - ly Thou_ art
1. the Lord.
2. most
high.
Emi7/A
Bmi/A
A
66 Rock (𝅗𝅥 =84-88) (in 2) (ad lib freely)
Solo
We come to praise_Your name_to - day,_ we want to serve_You in ev - 'ry way._
D
Bmi7
Emi7
Ami
G/B F/C G/C♯
(in octaves if possible)
(in 2)

Let the loud_ ho-san - nas ring,_ shout-ing the prais-es to God__ our King._ In the
Soprano
Alto
Tenor
Bass
D
Bmi7
Emi7
Ami7 G/B F/C G/C♯
74
name. In the name of the Son. In the name of the
Name_of the Fa - ther. Name_of the Son.
Name_of the Fa - ther. Name_of the Son.
Name_of the Fa - ther. Name_of the Son.
74
Dmi7
G
Dmi7
G
(in octaves if possible)

Ho-ly Ghost._ The Bless-ed Three in One._
Name_of the Ho-ly Ghost._ The Bless-ed Three_in One,_ the
Name_of the Ho-ly Ghost._ The Bless-ed Three_in One,_ the
Name_of the Ho-ly Ghost._ The Bless-ed Three_in One,_ the
Dmi7 G D/F♯ Emi7 D/F♯ Emi7/G D/F♯
chorus begins claps on beats 2&4
Oh_ A-men! men!
Bless-ed Three in One._ A-men! men!
Bless-ed Three_in One._ A-men! men!
Bless-ed Three_in One._ A-men! men!
Emi7 D/F♯ Emi7/G G/A 1 D Ami G/B F/C G/C♯ 2 D

III. CREDO
I BELIEVE IN GOD

ROBERT RAY

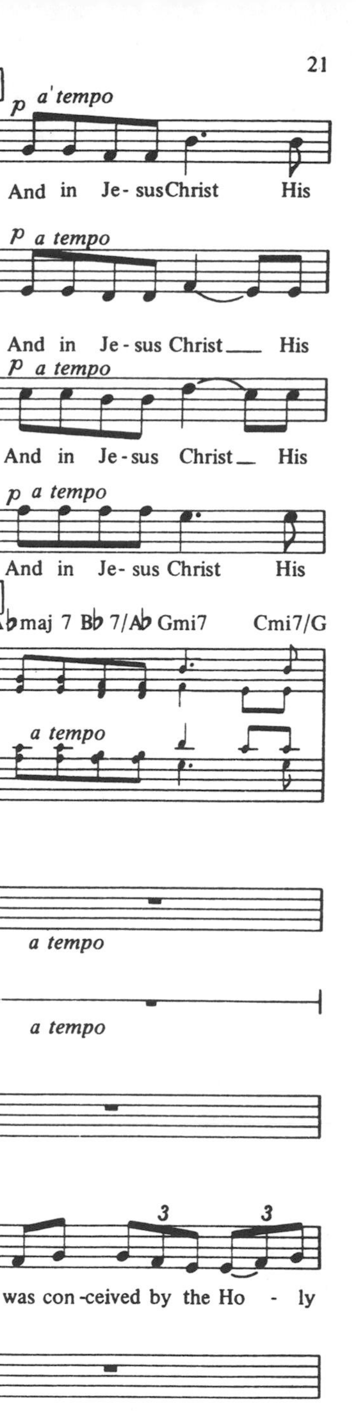
12
rit.
p a'tempo
And in Je-sus Christ His
heav - en and earth.
p a tempo
And in Je-sus Christ His
And in Je-sus Christ His
And in Je-sus Christ His
Fmi7/Bb Bb7(b9) Eb
ten. 8va
Abmaj 7 Bb7/Ab Gmi7 Cmi7/G
freely rit.
a tempo
on-ly Son our Lord.
on-ly Son our Lord,
Solo f freely
Who was con-ceived,
Who was con-ceived by the Ho - ly
Fmi7 Bb9 Ebmaj9 Eb6
F9
Eb/F

p
Born of the Virgin Mary, suffer'd under Pontius
Ghost.
Born of the Virgin Mary, suffer'd under Pontius
Born of the Virgin Mary, suffer'd under Pontius
Born of the Virgin Mary, Lord, Pontius
Fmi9/B♭
B♭7(♭9)
Gmi7
G♭+(maj7)
Fmi7
Fmi7/B♭
for rehearsal only
C
rit.
Pilate, crucified, died and was buried, He descended into
Pilate, crucified, died and was buried, He descended into
Pilate, crucified, died and was buried, He descended into
Pilate, crucified, died and was buried, He descended into
E♭maj7
Gmi7
G♭+(maj7)
Fmi7
Gmi
B♭9

25 Gospel Rock (𝅗𝅥 =96)
hell.
hell.
hell.
hell.
E♭
25 Gospel Rock (𝅗𝅥 =96)
p
Hi-Hat
(with sticks)
p
On the third day He a - rose,
On the third day He a - rose,
On the third day He a - rose,
On the third day He a - rose,
Cmi7
Dmi/C
Cmi
Dmi/C
Cmi7
(if no bass is used continue 8th note pattern)

on the third day He a - rose,
on the third day He a - rose,
on the third day He a - rose,
on the third day He a - rose,
Cmi7
Dmi7/C
Cmi
Dmi/C
Cmi7
37
mf
on the third day He a - rose,
mf
on the third day He a - rose,
mf
on the third day He a - rose,
mf
on the third day He a - rose,
Gmi/C
37
F/C
Cmi7
F/C
Gmi/C
mf
mf
mf

on the third day He a - rose,
on the third day He a - rose,
on the third day He a - rose,
on the third day He a - rose,
Gmi/C F/C Cmi7 F/C Gmi/C
45
on the third day He a - rose,
on the third day He a - rose,
on the third day He a - rose,
on the third day He a - rose,
Gmi/C Cmi 45 B♭/C A♭/C B♭/C Cmi

on the third
day
He a - rose.
on the third
day
He a - rose.
on the third
day
He a - rose.
on the third
day
He a - rose.
Cmi
Cmi
B♭/C
A♭/C
B♭/C
C
53
Solo
mf
He as-cend-ed to heav - en,
from death He was set free.
53
Fmi9
B♭9
Gmi9
C7(♭9)
mf
Cr. Cym.
mf (Ride Cym. on dome)
mf
(fast rock time)

Now He sits at the right hand and He's wait-in' for you and me.
C7(♭9)
Fmi9
B♭9
Gmi7
C9
61
p
He will judge all the world.
He will judge all the world.
He will judge all the world.
He will judge all the world.
C9
61 A♭/B♭

He will judge you and me.
He will judge you and me.
He will judge you and me.
He will judge you and me.
Ab/Bb
(Abmaj7/Bb) Bb7
fill
69
f div.
I be-lieve in the Ho-ly Spir-it and the Ho-ly cath-o-lic church.
optional text: Church U-ni-ver-sal on earth.
f
I be-lieve in the Ho-ly Spir-it and the Ho-ly cath-o-lic church.
optional text: Church U-ni-ver-sal on earth.
Eb
Ab/Eb
Eb
Ab/Eb
69
(ad lib 2nd time)
f
(ad lib 2nd time)
f (2nd time only)
f

I be- lieve_Lord in one bap - tism_ for the re- mis - sion of sin_ and re - birth.
I be- lieve_Lord in one bap - tism_ for the re- mis - sion of sin_ and re - birth.
I be lieve_Lord in one bap - tism_ for the re- mis - sion of sin_ and re - birth.
E♭
A♭/E♭
E♭
A♭/E♭
77
I be - lieve_ in the res - ur - rec - tion and the com - mun - ion of saints_ in this world.
div.
I be - lieve_ in the res - ur - rec - tion and the com - mun - ion of saints_ in this world.
77
E♭
A♭/E♭
E♭
A♭/E♭

I be-lieve_when my life is o-ver I'm go-ing home_just to live___with my God.
I be-lieve_when my life is o-ver I'm go-ing home_just to live___with my God.
I be lieve_when my life is o-ver I'm go-ing home_just to live___with my God.
Eb
Ab/Eb
Eb
85
p
I be-lieve,___
I be-lieve,___
I be-lieve,___
I be-lieve,___
I be-lieve,___
I be-lieve,___
I be-lieve,___
I be-lieve,___
85
Ab maj7
R.H.
L.H.
L.H.
Gmi7
C+7
C7

f div.
I be-lieve, I be-lieve, I be-
I be-lieve, I be-lieve, I be-
I be-lieve, I be-lieve, I be-
I be-lieve, I be-lieve, I be-
Abmaj7
R.H.
L.H.
L.H.
Gmi7
C+7
C7
Fmi7/Ab Gmi
93
-lieve in God and in the Ho-ly Ghost. I be-
-lieve in God and in the Ho-ly Ghost. I be-
-lieve in God and in the Ho-ly Ghost. I be-
-lieve in God and in the Ho-ly Ghost. I be-
93
Fmi7
Ebmaj7/G
Ab6
Fmi7/Ab Gmi
Fmi7
Ebmaj7/G
Ab6
Fmi7/Ab Gmi

back to pg 28
1
- lieve,
I be - lieve in God.
Fmi7
1 Fmi7/B♭
E♭
(drums enter 1st time)
2
rit.
I be - lieve in God.
2 Fmi7/B♭
(opt. fill)
fill
rit.

IV. ACCLAMATION
HALLELUJAH PRAISE THE LORD

ROBERT RAY

- lu - jah.
Hal - le -
Hal - le - lu - jah; Praise the Lord.
Hal - le -
Hal - le - lu - jah; Praise the Lord.
Hal - le -
Hal - le - lu - jah; Praise the Lord.
Hal - le -
E♭maj7
Fmi7
Gmi7
F♯mi7(♭9)
(A♭Gmi7)
Toms fill
13
To Coda
- lu - jah. Let us praise the
- lu - jah. Let us praise the
- lu - jah. Let us praise the
div.
- lu - jah. Let us praise the
13
Fmi9
4
B♭7(♭9)
To Coda
Toms

1.
Lord.
Hal - le -
Lord.
Lord.
Lord.
1.
E♭maj7
Fmi9
Gmi7
Fmi9
fill
2.
Lord.
Lord.
Lord.
Lord.
2.
E♭maj7
E♭maj7 B♭7/E♭ E♭maj7
E♭mi9/B♭
B♭mi9
E♭7
D♭/F Gmi7
fill

25
f
Praise Him with stringed in - stru - ments.
Praise Him with stringed in - stru - ments.
Praise Him with stringed in - stru - ments.
Praise Him with stringed in - stru - ments.
25
A♭maj7
B♭/A♭
Gmi7
Cmi7
Praise Him with dance.
Praise Him with dance.
Praise Him with dance.
Praise Him with dance.
Fmi7
(A♭/B♭ (B♭13 A♭/B♭)
E♭maj7
E♭7
D♭/F Gmi7

33
Praise Him on the psal - t'ry and harp.
Praise Him on the psal - t'ry and harp.
Praise Him on the psal - t'ry and harp.
Praise Him on the psal - t'ry and harp.
33
A♭maj7
B♭/A♭
Gmi7
C7
p
Ev - 'ry - thing that has breath
p
Ev - 'ry - thing that has breath
p
Ev - 'ry - thing that has
p
Ev - 'ry - thing that has
Fmi7
for rehearsal only

D.S. al Coda
ought to praise Him. Hal - le
ought to praise Him.
breath ought to praise Him.
breath ought to praise Him.
Fmi9
Gmi7
A♭maj7
A♭mi7(♭5)
D.S. al Coda
Play
fill
CODA
43
(repeat as desired)
Lord.
(repeat as desired)
Lord.
(repeat as desired)
Lord.
(repeat as desired)
Lord.
CODA
43
(repeat as desired)
E♭maj7
E♭9/D♭
C
Dmi7
C9/E

rit. (last time only)
Hal - le - lu - jah. Let us praise
div.
(Fmi7 E♭maj9) Fmi9
4
Fmi9
51
the Lord.
B♭7(♭9)
Play
for rehearsal only
(soft mallets)

V. SANCTUS
HOLY, HOLY LORD GOD OF HOSTS

ROBERT RAY

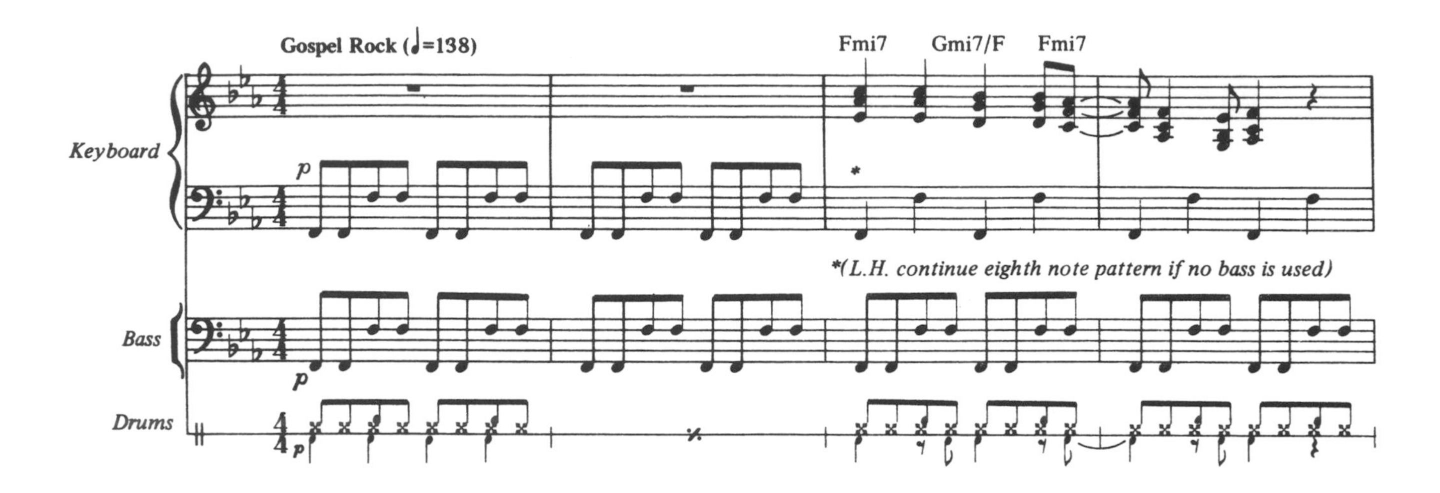

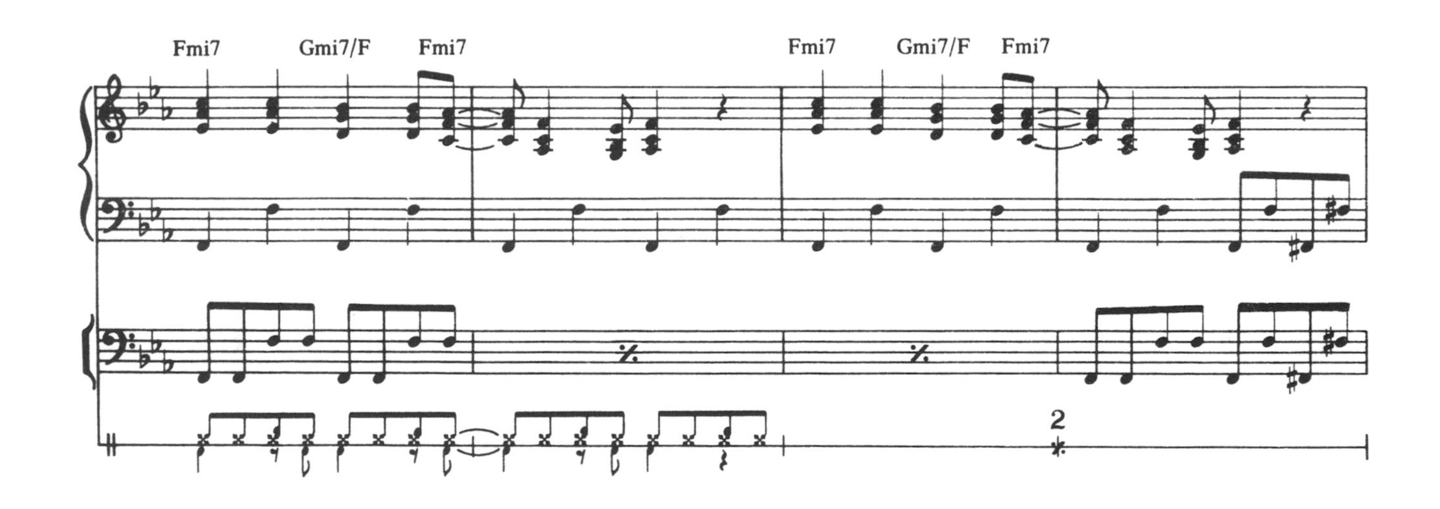

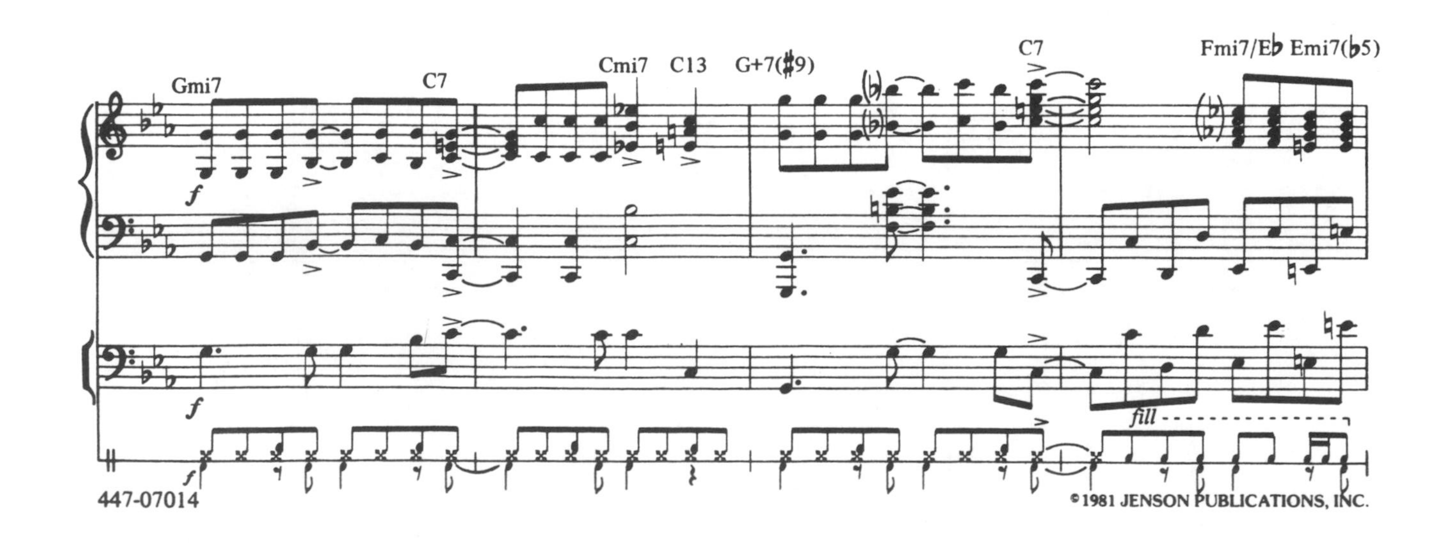

13
S
A
T
B
p
Ho - ly ho - ly Lord God of hosts. Ho - ly ho - ly Lord God of hosts.
Fmi7 Gmi7/F Fmi7
2
Ho - ly ho - ly Lord God of hosts.
in the high - est
Ho-san-na be- to Thee
G7
C
f
fill

23
Who gave me vic - to - ry.
Who gave me vic - to - ry.
p
Who gave me vic - to - ry.
1. There was a man sit-tin' by the
2. An-oth-er man lay by a
Who gave me vic - to - ry.
23
Cmi9 Bmi9 B♭mi9
road-side;
pool-side;
1. he was blind he could not see.
(Tenor Solo 2nd time)
2. thir - ty - eight years with his in - fir - mi - ty.
Fmi7
B♭mi9
Fmi7

f
1. Look'd a-round say-ing
2. Jump'd for joy say-ing
1. Look'd a-round say-ing
2. Jump'd for joy say-ing
Then the Mas- ter of the earth and skies;— touch'd his eyes and— he
Then the Lord trou- bled the wa - ter;— the man a - rose and— he
B♭mi9
Fmi7
G7
C
fill
31
p
Ho - ly ho - ly Lord— God of hosts. Ho - ly ho - ly Lord— God of hosts.
Fmi7
Gmi7/F
2

Ho - ly ho - ly Lord — God of hosts.
in the high - est
Ho - ly ho - ly Lord — God of hosts.
in the high - est
Ho - ly ho - ly Lord — God of hosts.
Ho-san-na be — to — Thee —
Ho - ly ho - ly Lord — God of hosts.
Ho-san-na be — to — Thee —
Fmi7
Gmi7/F
Fmi7
G9
C
fill
41
Who gave me vic - to - ry. —
Bless-ed is —
He who comes — in the
Who gave me vic - to - ry. —
He who comes — in the
Who gave me vic - to - ry. —
He who comes — in the
Who gave me vic - to - ry. —
He who comes — in the
G7
C
B♭/C
C7
B♭maj7
C/B♭
41

name of the Lord, we will al - ways sing,
name of the Lord, we will al - ways sing,
name of the Lord, we will al - ways sing,
name of the Lord, we will al - ways sing,
Ami7 Dmi7 B♭maj7 Ami7 Gmi7
al - ways sing Thy praise, sing Thy praise. Ho -
al - ways sing Thy praise, sing Thy praise. Ho -
al - ways sing Thy praise, sing Thy praise.
al - ways sing Thy praise, sing Thy praise.
(Gmi7) Gmi7/C Gmi7/F Fmaj7 Gmi7/F F9

49
-san - na in the high - est.
-san - na in the high - est.
-san - na in the high - est.
-san - na in the high - est.
49 B♭maj7
C/B♭
Ami7
Dmi
f
Sing ho - san - na,
ho - san - na
f
Sing ho - san - na,
ho - san - na
f
Ho - san - na,
f
Ho - san - na,
Dmi7
Gmi7
G♯o
F/A
fill

in the high - est.
in the high - est.
ho - san - na
in the high - est.
ho - san - na
in the high - est.
B♭6
B°
59
Like the blind man and the lame man,
C9
Bmi9
B♭mi9
Fmi7

I was lost, liv- ing in sin.
Then I o-pened up my
Bbmi9
Fmi7
Bbmi9
Now I shout say - ing
Now I shout say - ing
heart one day,—
I let the Sav - ior— in.
Fmi7
G7
C
fill

67
p
Ho - ly ho - ly Lord God of hosts. Ho - ly ho - ly Lord
Ho - ly ho - ly Lord God of hosts. Ho - ly ho - ly Lord
Ho - ly ho - ly Lord God of hosts. Ho - ly ho - ly Lord
Ho - ly ho - ly Lord God of hosts. Ho - ly ho - ly Lord
Fmi7 Gmi7/F Fmi7 Fmi7 Gmi7/F Fmi7
God of hosts. Ho - ly ho - ly Lord God of hosts.
God of hosts. Ho - ly ho - ly Lord God of hosts.
God of hosts. Ho - ly ho - ly Lord God of hosts.
God of hosts. Ho - ly ho - ly Lord God of hosts.
(Fmi7) Fmi7 Gmi7/F Fmi7

in the high - est
Who gave me vic - to - ry.
in the high - est
Who gave me vic - to - ry.
Ho - san - na be to Thee
Who gave me vic - to - ry.
Ho - san - na be to Thee
Who gave me vic - to - ry.
G7
C
G7
C
fill
77
f - p - f - ff - ff (vamp as desired)
Ho - ly ho - ly Lord Je - sus. Ho - ly!
f - p - f - ff - ff (vamp as desired)
Ho - ly ho - ly Lord Je - sus. Ho - ly!
f - p - f - ff - ff (vamp as desired)
Ho - ly ho - ly Lord Je - sus. Ho - ly!
f - p - f - ff - ff (vamp as desired)
Ho - ly ho - ly Lord Je - sus. Ho - ly!
Fmi7/E♭ Emi7(♭5)
77
Fmi7
Gmi/D Fmi7/E♭ C9/E
f - p - f - ff - ff (vamp as desired)
fill
f - p - f - ff - ff (vamp as desired)
f - p - f - ff - ff

VI. AGNUS DEI
LAMB OF GOD

ROBERT RAY

447-07014

10
All sopranos 1st time
mer - cy on us. Lamb of God who takes a- way the
mer - cy on us.
tenors 2nd time
mer - cy on us. Lamb of God who takes a- way the
mer - cy on us.
Dmi7 Emi7 Dmi7/F F/G G7 5
10
C G/B
(Tom) (Cym.) (Closed Hi-Hat)
*(rim knocks)
sins of the world, have mer - cy on us, have
have mer - cy on us, have
sins of the world, have mer - cy on us, have
have mer - cy on us, have
Ami7 Emi7 Dmi7 Emi7 Dmi/F Emi7

div.
19 slightly faster
mer - cy on us.
slightly faster
All tenors
Solo
slightly faster
1. For You came to die for
2. In Your word You showed us
slightly faster
Dmi7 Emi7 Fmaj7 Dmi7/G G7
19 B♭
F/A
slightly faster
fill
slightly faster
rit.
me, suf fer'd, bled, and died, died on Cal - va -
how, we are try - ing Lord, hear our pray'r right
Fmaj7/G G7(♭9)
B♭
F/A
Fmi6/A♭

54
back on to pg 51
rit.
a tempo
26
p
ten.
Lamb of God who takes a-way the
* ad lib freely
ry.
now.
Gsus
12
R.H.
L.H.
Fmaj7/G
G7(♭9)
C(add 9)
Gsus/B
(soft mallets)
sins of the world,
grant us Thy peace,
Grant us Thy peace,
Ami 9
Emi7
Dmi7
Emi7 Dmi7/F
447-07014

34
div.
grant us Thy peace.
A - - men. A -
A - - - - - men. A - - -
A - - - - men.
A - men.
Dmi7 Emi7 Dmi7/F F/G G7
for rehearsal only

42
men.
A
men.
A
A
men.
A
A
men.
42
men.
A
men.
A
men.
men.
A
men.
A
men.
div.
men.
A
men.
A
men.
A
men.
A
men.
A
men.
pp
p
ppp
div.
(opt. div.)
ff
Csus
C
F/C
F/C
Fmi6
C
ff Play
(soft mallets)
*Instruments optional to end